Before I go to sleep

This book belongs to

....

....

Written by Ronne Randall
Illustrated by Tony Kerins

PRODUCED FOR CHAD VALLEY TOYS
489-499 Avebury Boulevard,
Central Milton Keynes, MK9 2NW

www.argos.co.uk

ISBN 978-1-4454-7522-6
Batch Code: S34511
Made in China

Before I go to sleep

Before I go to sleep,
Mummy brings my drink,
and kisses me
night-night.

Night-night,
Mummy.

Daddy reads me a story
about the little red sailboat.

Then he kisses me
night-night.

Night-night,
Daddy.

Where's Waggy dog?

There you are.
Night-night, Waggy dog.

Before I go to sleep,
I kiss Teddy night-night.

Night-night, Teddy.
Are you sleepy yet?

Kitty isn't sleepy yet.

I wonder where
she goes at night?

Before I go to sleep,
I'll snuggle down
and close my eyes.

Where is Teddy going?
Teddy and Waggy dog
are following Kitty.
Wait for me, I'll come too.

We'll sail away in our

little red sailboat

over Grandma and Grandpa's house

and across the pond to say,

Night-night, ducks. Night-night, sky.

Night-night, moon.

Night-night, stars.

Night-night, world.

Teddy, are you sleepy yet?
We're almost home, now.

Night-night, me.

Night-night, you.

Night-night, everyone.

Sweet dreams.